REVISION BOOK

Grade 5 Music Theory

to be used in conjunction with **All-In-One to Grade 5**

Comprehensive to the requirements of both ABRSM and Trinity Guildhall syllabuses

By Rachel Billings

Published by Aaron publications
www.aaronpublications.co.uk

Printed in Great Britain by Pelican Trust Ltd. Lincoln.

Preface

This revision booklet provides practice for topics covered in the Grade 5 syllabus for both Associated Board (ABRSM) and Trinity Guildhall exams and assumes knowledge of all previous grades. It is the last in a series of graded revision booklets which are designed to be used alongside 'All-In-One to Grade 5'. Many questions (especially those in the longer General Exercise section) test a pupil's comprehension of more than one topic at once and wording, wherever possible, is the same as that used by the relevant exam board so that students will feel well prepared and confident in the final stages before an exam.

Rachel Billings BMus, GRNCM, PgDip.

CONTENTS

Topics should be completed by all students except for the last chapter which need be completed by Trinity Guildhall students only.

CHAPTER ONE
NOTATION

TENOR CLEF
Notation and
Transposition of Octave

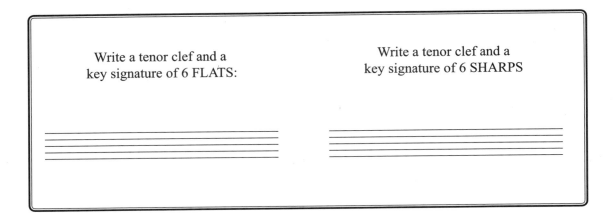

Write a tenor clef and a
key signature of 6 FLATS:

Write a tenor clef and a
key signature of 6 SHARPS

1. Rewrite the following passage at the same pitch using the tenor clef:

Dukas, The Sorcerer's Apprentice

a) **Vif**

J.S.Bach, 48 Preludes & Fugues Bk II (Fugue No. 18)

b)

2

2 a) Rewrite the following passage one
octave lower in the tenor clef:

Cezar Frank, 'Prelude, Choral et fugue' for Piano (Choral)

Poco più lento

Molto cantabile, non troppo dolce

b) Rewrite the following passage one octave higher in the tenor clef:

J.S.Bach, 48 Preludes & Fugues, Bk I (Fugue No.8)

3. Rewrite this passage at the same pitch using the given clef:

Grieg, The Lonely Wanderer, Op.43 No.2

4. Write the following passages one octave higher in the treble clef then one octave lower in the bass clef:

Stravinsky, Septet (Gigue)

a)

© Copyright 1953 by Hawkes & Son (London) Ltd.
Reproduced by permission of Boosey & Hawkes Music Publishers Ltd.

Adagio assai

Beethoven, Piano Trio, Op. 121a

b)

CHAPTER TWO
TIME

SIMPLE TIME, COMPOUND TIME & IRREGULAR TIME

Time Signatures and Irregular Divisions
(quintuplets, sextuplets, septuplets and nonuplets)

1. a) Add bar-lines to the following passages which all begin on the first beat of the bar.
   b) Circle an irregular time signature.

6

Chopin, Fantasy Impromptu, Op.66 No. 4

Henri Dutilleux, Sonatina for Flute and Piano

Vaughan Williams, Symphony No.4 (1st mvt)

Chopin, Polonaise No. 15 (Trio)

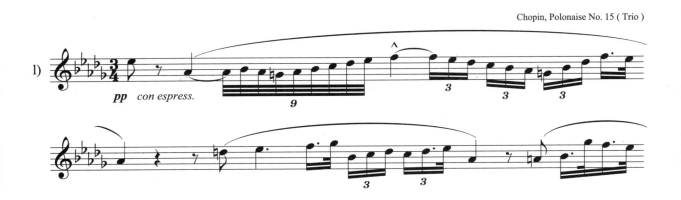

2. Add time signatures to the following passages.

3. Add the appropriate rest or rests at the places marked* to form a complete bar.

4. Write the following passage in notes and rests of *half* the value and add the new time signature required.

CHAPTER THREE
TONALITY

MAJOR & MINOR KEYS

Scales and Key Signatures

1 a) Write a key signature of three sharps and then one octave **descending** of the **harmonic** minor scale which has that key signature. Use semibreves (whole-notes), begin on the tonic and remember to put in any additional sharp, flat or natural signs.

b Using semibreves (whole-notes), write one octave **ascending** of the major scale that begins on the given note. Do not use a key signature but put in all necessary sharp or flat signs.

c) Put sharps or flats in front of the notes that need them to form the scale of E♭ flat **melodic** minor. Do not use a key signature but put in all necessary sharp or flat signs.

2. Add the correct clef, key signature, and any necessary accidentals to each of the following so as to form the scales named.

a)

G♯ harmonic minor

b)

C♯ melodic minor

c)

F♯ harmonic minor

3. Write each of the scales named, beginning on the requested note.

a) B minor, descending *without key signature*. Begin on the mediant.

b) B♭ melodic minor ascending and descending, *with key signature*. Begin on the submediant.

Compound Intervals (diatonic and chromatic)

What is a 'compound interval' ? ....

....

Give the full names of the following intervals which may include any diatonic, chromatic and compound interval. Keep in mind the key signature and any accidentals which may have occurred earlier in the bar.

Riesenberg, Piano Sonata No.2

a)

1. _____ 2. _____ 3. _____

4. _____ 5. _____ 6. _____

George Gershwin, Three Preludes (No.1)

b)

1. _____ 2. _____ 3. _____

4. _____ 5. _____ 6. _____

Alban Berg, Sonata Op.1

c)

1. _____ 2. _____ 3. _____

4. _____ 5. _____ 6. _____

J.S.Bach, Nun Komm, der Heiden Heiland

d)

1. _____ 2. _____ 3. _____

4. _____ 5. _____ 6. _____

Chord Inversions, Chord Symbols and Cadences

1. Name the key, identify the chords and their inversion using Roman numerals (e.g. Ia, Vb etc.). Name each final cadence.

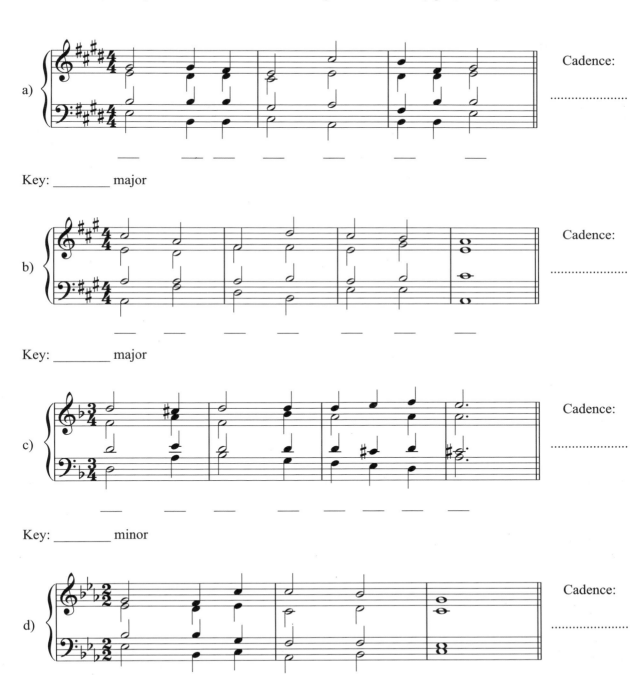

a) Key: _____ major   Cadence: ....

b) Key: _____ major   Cadence: ....

c) Key: _____ minor   Cadence: ....

d) Key: _____ major   Cadence: ....

e)

Cadence:

....

Key: _____ major

f)

Cadence:

....

Key: _____ minor

2. Suggest suitable cadential progressions in the following melody by indicating one chord (I ,II, IV or V) at each of the places marked A - E. The chords should be shown by ONE of the following methods:

a) by writing Roman symbols (e.g. I, II etc.) or Jazz symbols (e.g. C major, Em)

b) by writing notes on the staves.

FIRST CADENCE:

Chord A ....

Chord B ....

SECOND CADENCE:

Chord C ....

Chord D ....

Chord E ....

GENERAL EXERCISES

1. Compose a melody of not more than eight bars to the following words. Make sure that each syllable is clearly placed under the note/s to which it belongs. Indicate the appropriate speed and other necessary performance directions.

The Owl and the Pussy-Cat went to sea
In a beautiful pea-green boat:
They took some honey, and plenty of money
Wrapped up in a five-pound note.

'The Owl and the Pussy-Cat'
Edward Lear   1812-1888

2. This extract is from an orchestral piece by Elgar. Look at it and then answer the questions below.

a) Name the instrument for which this solo part is written. Give at least three reasons for your choice of instrument.

Instrument .... Reasons ....

....

....

b) To which family of orchestral instruments does this instrument belong? ....

c) i) Write bars two and three at the same pitch in the tenor clef.

ii) Answer TRUE or FALSE:

The tenor clef is another clef commonly used by the instrument for which this part is written. ....

18

d) Give the meaning of the following:

Lento	....	espress.	....
Ad lib.	....	arco.	....
Ten.	....	V	....
Rall.	....	∧	....
Sf.	....	⊓	....
A tempo	....	{	....

e) Describe fully the intervals in brackets marked *u, v, w, x, y* and *z.*

u ....   v ....   w ....

x ....   y ....   z ....

f) Identify the chords and their inversion at the places marked * by writing the appropritate chord symbol underneath the stave (e.g. Ib, Vc). The key is E minor.

g) Find the following notes and identify them by writing the appropriate letter above the note and circling the note.

A. Supertonic note
B. Subdominant note
C. Submediant note
D. Leading note

19

3. The following extract is from a work by R. Strauss for a solo Brass instrument and orchestra. The orchestral part has been arranged here for piano accompaniment.

a) i) Name the Brass instrument for which this solo part is written. Give a reason for your choice of instrument.

Instrument .... Reasons ....

....

....

ii) Name one Woodwind instrument with a similar range. ....

iii) What term is used to describe a work written for a solo instrument and orchestra?

....

b) i) Name the key of the piece from bar 4 onwards. Key ....

   ii) Complete the time signature at the beginning of the extract.
   iii) Describe the time signature as simple or compound, duple, triple or quadruple.

   ....

c) Give the meaning of the following musical terms and circle one which best suits the tempo of the melody
   at the given metronome speed (♪ = 69)

   Sehr lebhaft..   Ziemlich ....

   Simile   ....   Lacrimoso ....

   Ped.   ....   Smorzando ....

d) i) Write the following passage enharmonically using the appropriate key signature.
   ii) Name the new key and cadence formed by the notes you have written.

   Cadence ....

   Key ....

   iii) Name two other cadences (*different* from your answer to question "dii") and chord progression/s they
        may use. The first has been completed as an example.

   ....*Plagal*.................... cadence ....IV - I........................... chord progression

   .... cadence .... chord progression

   .... cadence .... chord progression

e) i) Explain the meaning of 6   found in bars 4-6 ....
   ii) Explain the meaning of 3   found in bars 4-6 ....

4. The following passage shows the clarinet and bassoon parts from Mozart's Serenade K. 375

a) i) To which family of orchestral instruments do the clarinet and bassoon belong?

....

ii) Name three other instruments which belong to the same family.

....

....

....

b) Why do the two staves use different key signatures? ....

....

....

c) i) Name a standard orchestral instrument with a range similar to the clarinet. ....

ii) Name a standard orchestral instrument with a range similar to the bassoon. ....

d) Describe fully the intervals in brackets marked *u, v, w, x, y* and *z*.

u .... v .... w ....

x .... y .... z ....

e) Rewrite bars 1-3 in open score with the clarinet parts at concert pitch.

f) Write the musical terms for the following words which describe how this piece should be played. Use German, Italian or French words as instructed.

German for ... Cheerful/ joyful...

With movement...

Italian for... Rhythmically...

Joking/ playful ....

French for... Happy...

Lively/ quick...

g) Complete:

single/ double

The bassoon is a .... reed instrument. Other instruments with the same type of

reed are the .... , ... and .... Of these instruments, the

interval   higher/ lower

.... is the only transposing instrument and sounds ....than written.

5. Complete a melody which is no more than 8 bars in total, using each of the given openings. Choose from one of the instruments named and *indicate whether your chosen instrument is at transposed pitch or concert pitch*. You may change the clef if it is appropriate for the selected instrument. All performance directions should be included.

a)

Chosen instrument _____

For violin or trumpet

b)

Chosen instrument _____

For oboe or horn

TRINITY GUILDHALL EXAMS ONLY[1]

1. Name the following scale.

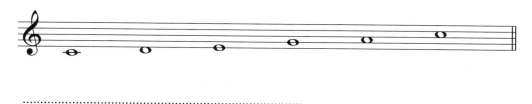

....

2. Name the following intervals. Then write their inversions and name them.

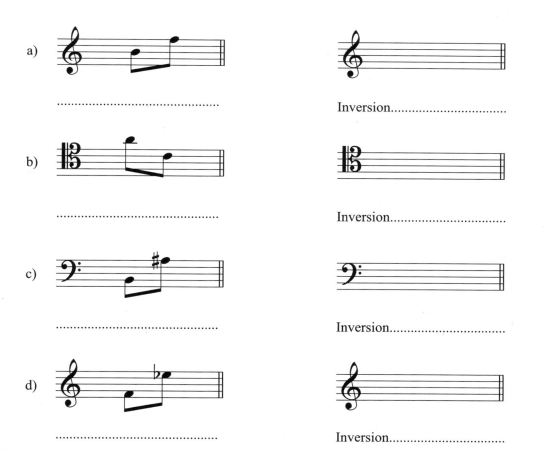

a)

.... Inversion..............................

b)

.... Inversion..............................

c)

.... Inversion..............................

d)

.... Inversion..............................

[1] Topics are for Trinity Guildhall students only. However the use of key signatures here (and throughout this booklet) corresponds to the ABRSM syllabus and in this respect exceeds Trinity Guildhall requirements.

3. Label the following broken chords (For example: 'F minor' or 'C major').

....

....

4. Write diminished supertonic triads in the following keys and include any necessary accidentals.

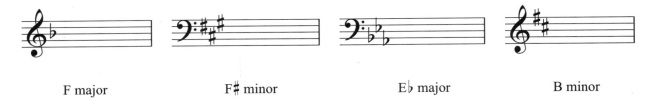

F major   F♯ minor   E♭ major   B minor

5. Label the chords and their inversions with Roman numerals below the stave and jazz chord symbols above to show the chord progression.

G minor

6. Using crotchets, write out 4-part chords for SATB using the chords shown by the Roman numerals. Double the root wherever possible, even if the chord is in root, first or second inversion.

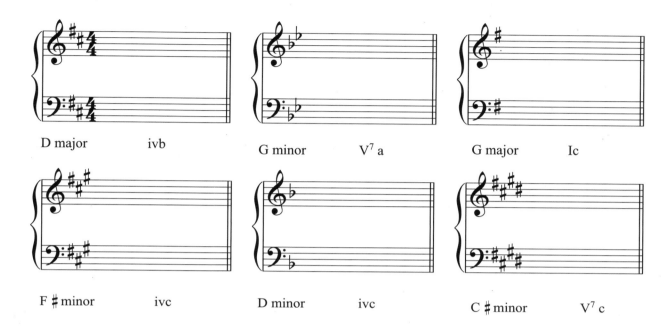

7 a) Use the root, first or second inversion of each triad shown by the chord symbols to write a bass line. Circle an auxiliary note.

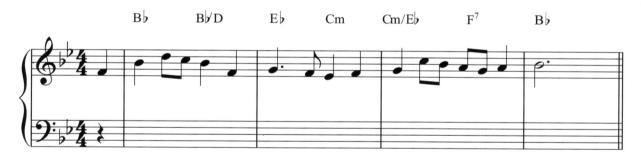

b) Use notes from the chords shown by the chord symbols to write a tune above the bass line. Decorate your tune once you have the main harmony notes in place.

8 a) Transpose the following melody down a major 6th, using an appropriate clef.

Mendelssohn, Op. 7 No.2

Name an instrument popular in jazz bands, which sounds a major 6th lower than its written notes.

....

b) Transpose the following melody up a minor 7th, using an appropriate clef.

J.S. Bach, 48 Preludes & Fugues, BkII (Fugue No.20)

c) Transpose the following melody up a minor 2nd.

Tchaikovsky, 'The Seasons' (April: Snowdrop)